THE CHRISTMAS STORY
AN ADVENT BOOK WITH STAND-UP MANGER

· ·

PICTURES BY SHEILA MOXLEY

TangoBooks

Long ago, in the city of Nazareth in the land of Judea, there lived a young woman whose name was Mary. She was engaged to marry a carpenter, Joseph.

God sent the angel Gabriel with a message for Mary. "Greetings," he said. "Do not be afraid! God has chosen you to give birth to a son, whom you will name Jesus. He will be called the Son of God and his kingdom will last forever."

In those days Emperor Caesar Augustus ordered that all the world should be taxed. Joseph had to return to his own city, Bethlehem, to be taxed.

He went with Mary, who was expecting her child.

Bethlehem was full of people who had come to be taxed.

While they were there, the time came for Mary to have her baby.

When Jesus was born, Mary wrapped him up warmly and laid him in a manger, because there was no room for them in the inn.

There were shepherds in the fields nearby,
keeping watch over their flocks through the night.

An angel of the Lord appeared to them and they were filled with fear. But the angel said, "Do not be afraid. I bring you great news. Today a Saviour has been born in Bethlehem, who is Christ the Lord. You will find him lying in a manger."

Suddenly the sky was filled with angels saying,
"Glory to God in the highest and on earth peace
to people of good will."

The shepherds said to one another, "Come, let us go to Bethlehem to see this thing that has happened." And there they found Mary, Joseph, and the baby, just as the angel had said.

When Jesus was born, three wise men from the east looked to the heavens.

They saw a bright star and prepared for a long journey west.

At last they came to the city of
Jerusalem in Judea. "Where is he
who has been born king of the
Jews?" they asked. "For we have
seen his star and have come to
worship him."

Wicked Herod was king of Judea. When he heard about this child king, he was very worried.

He met with the wise men secretly and told them to look for the baby. "Search for him," said Herod, "and when you have found him, bring me word, so that I may go myself and worship him."

After they had heard the king, the wise men went on their way, and the star they had seen in the east went ahead of them.

19

The star stopped over the place where the child was and when the wise men saw it, they were overjoyed. They entered and saw the baby with his mother Mary and they knelt down and worshipped him. Then they gave him gifts of gold, frankincense, and myrrh.

And because they were warned by God not to go back to Herod, they returned to their own country by another way.